Bible Search & Find

Tony Tallarico

Kidsbooks®

Copyright © 2006 Kidsbooks, LLC and Tony Tallarico
www.kidsbooks.com

All rights reserved including the right
of reproduction in whole or in part in any form.

Manufactured in the United States of America

Search & Find is a registered trademark of Kidsbooks, LLC.

0806-1K

Visit us at **www.kidsbooks.com**®

CONTENTS

INTRODUCTION

Introduce the young readers in your life to the Bible with this fun, engaging, and richly illustrated collection of tales. We've combined the timeless stories of the Bible with fun search-and-find activities. Children will be drawn into learning about God, Adam and Eve, Moses, Jesus, the apostles, the Good Samaritan, and much, much more.

Bible Search & Find® helps sharpen a child's reading, concentration, and cognitive skills. Careful searching for hidden objects will enhance visual dexterity, while reading the stories will help develop reading comprehension and instill a strong sense of values.

This interactive presentation of the Bible will provide hours of enjoyment and a rewarding reading experience for the whole family.

GENESIS

God created the world in six days. He created the heavens and sun and stars, and all of Earth's plants and animals. From the dust of Earth, God created man and called him Adam. For Adam, God planted a beautiful garden in Eden. One day, God saw that Adam was lonely. So He made a woman. Adam called her Eve. After God created Eve, He rested. This day is called the sabbath, which means "to stop."

Learn about Genesis as you Search & Find® these items:

Birds (3)	Fish (2)	Mushroom	Ring
Bone	Flame	Owl	Rooster
Buffalo	Flowerpot	Pig	Shovel
Cat	Giraffe	Rabbits (2)	Squirrel
Duck	Mouse	Rain cloud	Worm

THE GARDEN OF EDEN WAS ADAM AND EVE'S HOME.

THE EARTH WAS A PARADISE.

ADAM AND EVE WERE VERY HAPPY IN EDEN.

IN EDEN THE SUN SHONE GENTLY ON DELICIOUS FRUIT TREES.

GOD SAYS THAT WE CAN EAT THE FRUIT FROM ALL THE TREES EXCEPT THIS ONE.

THE FRUIT THAT GREW ON THE TREE OF KNOWLEDGE OF GOOD AND EVIL WAS FORBIDDEN.

ADAM AND EVE WERE CURIOUS ABOUT THE TREE OF KNOWLEDGE, BUT THEY STAYED AWAY FROM THE FRUIT.

IMMEDIATELY ADAM AND EVE WERE ASHAMED. EVE TOLD GOD THAT THE SNAKE HAD TRICKED HER.

ONE DAY THE SNAKE CAME TO EVE AND CONVINCED HER TO EAT THE FORBIDDEN FRUIT.

EVE TOOK A BITE AND GAVE SOME TO ADAM.

NOAH AND THE ARK

Many, many years after God made Earth, He looked down from heaven and was not happy. Everywhere He looked people were fighting and hurting each other. They were hurting Earth, too. God decided to clear out all the people by flooding Earth. There was one man that God wanted to spare. His name was Noah. God told Noah to build a big boat called an ark. Noah was to make it large enough to hold one male and one female of every animal on Earth.

NOAHS ARK WAS 450 FEET LONG, 75 FEET WIDE AND 40 FEET HIGH.

THAT'S A GOOD HEIGHT.

THE ARK HAD 3 DECKS, A ROOF ON TOP, AND A DOOR ON ITS SIDE.

GOD SENT A WARM GENTLE WIND TO DRY THE EARTH.

FOR 150 DAYS, THE FLOODS WASHED OVER EVEN THE HIGHEST MOUNTAINS.

NOAH AND HIS FAMILY GATHERED TWO OF EVERY LIVING CREATURE, ONE MALE AND ONE FEMALE, INTO THE ARK.

THEN GOD STARTED THE RAIN. IT RAINED FOR 40 DAYS AND 40 NIGHTS, FLOODING ALL THE EARTH.

I'M THIRSTY.

TWO BY TWO, CAMELS, LIONS, ELEPHANTS, BEARS, SNAKES, BIRDS OF EVERY KIND, AND EVEN THE TINIEST INSECTS WERE HURRIED ON BOARD.

GOD REMINDED NOAH TO BRING LOTS OF FOOD FOR HIS FAMILY AND ALL THE CREATURES.

I THINK WE ARE LATE.

THIS MUST BE THE PLACE.

WE SHOULD HAVE STARTED EARLIER.

Learn about Noah and the ark as you Search & Find® these items:

Bucket	Hammer
Candle	Lions (2)
Cat	Mice (2)
Deer	Olive branch
Doe	Owls (2)
Elephants (2)	Saw
Giraffes (2)	Umbrella

12

THE TOWER OF BABEL

One day, the people of the city of Babylon decided to build a great tower. They wanted to make a tower that would reach up into heaven.

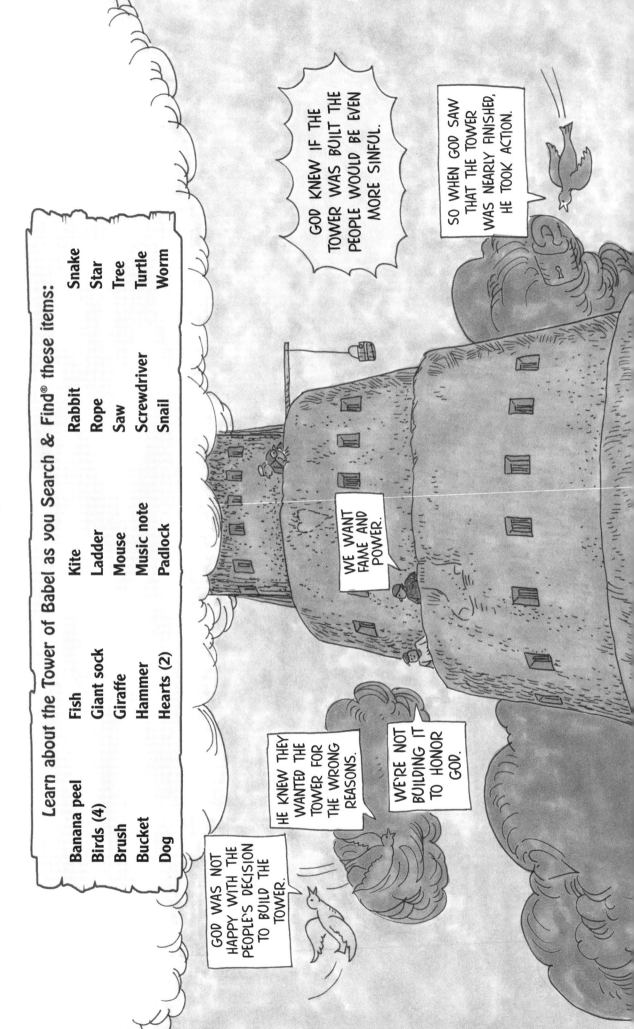

Learn about the Tower of Babel as you *Search & Find*® these items:

Banana peel	Fish	Kite	Rabbit	Snake
Birds (4)	Giant sock	Ladder	Rope	Star
Brush	Giraffe	Mouse	Saw	Tree
Bucket	Hammer	Music note	Screwdriver	Turtle
Dog	Hearts (2)	Padlock	Snail	Worm

THE PATIENCE OF JOB

Job was a rich, kind man who had ten children. His fields were full of grains and vegetables, and he owned many animals.

Learn about Job as you Search & Find® these items:

Arrow	Flowerpot	Oilcan
Axe	Flying bat	Sailboat
Backpack	Hammer	Scarecrow
Birdbath	Heart	Seal
Bone	Jack-o'-lantern	Star
Broom	Key	Toothbrush
Bucket	Lost kite	Turtle

JOB LOVED GOD AND ALWAYS TRIED TO PLEASE HIM.

ONE DAY, SATAN TOLD GOD THAT JOB WAS NOT REALLY GOOD.

SATAN SAID IT WAS EASY FOR JOB TO LOVE GOD BECAUSE JOB WAS RICH.

GOD BELIEVED THAT JOB WOULD NOT CURSE HIM, NO MATTER HOW JOB WAS MISTREATED. SO GOD ALLOWED SATAN TO TEST JOB BY TORMENTING HIM.

FIRST SATAN KILLED ALL OF JOB'S CATTLE, SERVANTS, CAMELS, AND SHEPHERDS.

I BRING YOU TERRIBLE NEWS. ALL OF YOUR CHILDREN HAVE BEEN KILLED, AND YOUR HOME WAS DESTROYED.

THEN SATAN MADE JOB SICK. SORES BROKE OUT ALL OVER JOB'S BODY.

JOB SAT ON THE GROUND IN A PILE OF ASHES.

JOB WAS VERY SAD, BUT HE DID NOT TURN HIS BACK ON GOD.

ABRAHAM AND ISAAC

Abraham was the father of the Hebrew nation. While other people worshiped many gods, Abraham worshiped only one God. God appeared to Abraham and said, "Take your family to a new country, and I will make you a great nation."

Learn about Abraham and Isaac as you Search & Find® these items:

Arrow	Donkey	Jug	Paintbrush
Birds (3)	Egg	Key	Snail
Bone	Fish (2)	Kite	Toothbrush
Butterfly	Frog	Lamb	Turtle
Cup	Hearts (2)	Nut	Worm

ABRAHAM TRAVELED TO CANAAN. HE TOOK WITH HIM HIS WIFE, SARAH, AND HIS BROTHER'S SON, LOT.

ABRAHAM'S DESCENDANTS BECAME KNOWN AS THE HEBREWS BECAUSE THEY WERE ORIGINALLY FROM HEBRON.

ABRAHAM AND SARAH HAD A SON.

GOD TOLD ABRAHAM AND SARAH TO NAME THE BABY ISAAC, WHICH MEANS "LAUGHTER."

ISAAC WAS BORN WHEN SARAH WAS 90 YEARS OLD AND ABRAHAM WAS 100.

ABRAHAM LOVED HIS SON VERY MUCH. HE ALSO LOVED GOD VERY MUCH.

GOD WANTED TO KNOW IF ABRAHAM LOVED HIM MORE THAN HE LOVED ISAAC.

GOD DECIDED TO TEST ABRAHAM'S FAITH. HE ASKED ABRAHAM TO KILL ISAAC.

SODOM AND GOMORRAH

...ham was resting near his tent. He looked up and saw ...ward him. It was God and two of His messengers. Abraham ...em food and water. As they rested under the tree, God ...am His plan to destroy two cities: Sodom and Gomorrah.

...arn about Sodom and Gomorrah ...s you Search & Find® these items:

Axe	Cricket	Pear
Bell	Fish	Saw
Birds (4)	Fork	Snail
Bow	Frog	Stars (2)
	Hammer	Turtles (2)
	Heart	Worm
	Horseshoe	
	Mouse	

GOD SAID THAT THE PEOPLE OF THESE CITIES WERE REALLY BAD.

ABRAHAM'S NEPHEW, LOT, LIVED IN SODOM. TO SAVE LOT'S LIFE, ABRAHAM TRIED TO PERSUADE GOD NOT TO DESTROY THE CITIES.

ABRAHAM ASKED GOD TO SPARE THE CITY OF SODOM IF HE COULD FIND TEN GOOD PEOPLE THERE.

GOD AGREED.

THE MESSENGERS DECIDED THAT THERE WERE NOT TEN GOOD PEOPLE IN SODOM; ONLY LOT AND HIS FAMILY WERE GOOD.

GOD SENT TWO ANGELS DISGUISED AS MEN TO SEE LOT AND TO FIND OTHER GOOD PEOPLE.

LOT WAS A GOOD MAN AND OFFERED THE TRAVELERS FOOD AND A PLACE TO REST.

LOT DID NOT KNOW THAT THE MEN WERE ANGELS SENT BY GOD. HE THOUGHT THEY WERE SIMPLE TRAVELERS PASSING THROUGH THE CITY.

THE OTHER PEOPLE OF SODOM WERE NOT GOOD. THEY TRIED TO HARM THE TRAVELERS WHO WERE VISITING LOT.

20

21

ESAU AND JACOB

Isaac, Abraham's son, was 40 years old when he married a beautiful young woman named Rebecca. Rebecca and Isaac had twin sons. Esau was born first. Jacob was born second, holding on to Esau's heel.

Learn about Esau and Jacob as you Search & Find® these items:

Apple	Envelope
Arrow	Fish (4)
Barrel	Four-leaf
Bone	clover
Bow	Heart
Broom	Mushroom
Candle	Octopus
Cat	Pie
Crayons (2)	Ring
Dogs (2)	Stocking
Drum	Turtle (2)

THE NAME JACOB MEANS "HEEL."

I'VE BROUGHT MEAT FOR FATHER TO EAT.

I LIKE TO WORK IN THE GARDEN AT HOME.

EVEN THOUGH THEY WERE TWINS, THE BROTHERS WERE VERY DIFFRENT.

THEY DID NOT LOOK ALIKE, AND THEY LIKED DIFFRENT THINGS.

ESAU GREW TO BE TALL AND BROAD. HE WAS ALSO VERY HAIRY.

JACOB GREW TO BE TALL AND THIN. HE HAD SMOOTH SKIN.

ESAU WAS ENERGETIC AND LIKED TO PLAY OUTDOORS AND HUNT.

JACOB WAS QUIET AND ENJOYED STAYING INDOORS WITH HIS MOTHER.

ESAU WAS ISAAC'S FAVORITE SON.

JACOB WAS REBECCA'S FAVORITE SON.

AS THE FIRST BORN, ESAU WAS TO INHERIT ISAAC'S LAND, GOODS, AND ANIMALS.

HE WOULD ALSO RULE OVER JACOB.

ONE DAY ESAU CAME HOME FROM THE FIELD VERY HUNGRY.

ESAU BEGGED JACOB FOR A BOWL OF HIS STEW.

JACOB AGREED TO GIVE ESAU STEW BUT ONLY IF ESAU GAVE HIM HIS FIRSTBORN RIGHTS.

FAINT WITH HUNGER, ESAU AGREED, BUT HE DID NOT PLAN TO HONOR THE AGREEMENT.

23

JOSEPH AND THE COAT OF MANY COLORS

Jacob settled in Canaan with his wife Leah and his twelve sons. Jacob loved his eleventh son, Joseph, the most because he was born when Jacob was very old. Jacob made Joseph a special long coat woven with many beautiful colors.

Learn about Joseph as you Search & Find® these items:

Arrow	Frog	Slingshot	Wheel
Axe	Heart	Snake	Worm
Basket	Jugs (2)	Star	
Birds (3)	Lost sandal	Sword	
Bone	Oil lamp	Turtle	
Bow	Rabbit		
Fish (2)	Ring		
Fishing Pole	Shovel		

JACOB'S OTHER SONS WERE VERY JEALOUS OF JOSEPH.

THEY WANTED TO HAVE A COAT OF MANY COLORS, TOO.

TO MAKE MATTERS WORSE, JOSEPH TOLD HIS BROTHERS HE HAD DREAMED THAT ONE DAY THEY WOULD ALL BOW DOWN TO HIM.

HIS BROTHERS DID NOT LIKE THIS.

ONE DAY JOSEPH WENT TO SEE HIS BROTHERS IN THE FIELDS WHERE THEY WERE LOOKING AFTER THE SHEEP.

WHEN THE BROTHERS SAW JOSEPH THEY WANTED TO HURT HIM.

JOSEPH WAS TAKEN TO EGYPT.

REUBEN, ONE OF THE BROTHERS, SUGGESTED THAT THEY THROW JOSEPH INTO AN EMPTY WELL. THE BROTHERS AGREED.

REUBEN PLANNED TO COME BACK AND RESCUE JOSEPH. BUT BEFORE HE COULD, THE OTHER BROTHERS SOLD JOSEPH TO SLAVE TRADERS.

MOSES : PART I

Joseph's family prospered and they became a powerful Hebrew tribe in Egypt. After Joseph's death, a cruel new pharaoh came to power. He forced all the Hebrews, including Joseph's family, to work as slaves. Pharaoh also ordered that all the Hebrew baby boys be drowned.

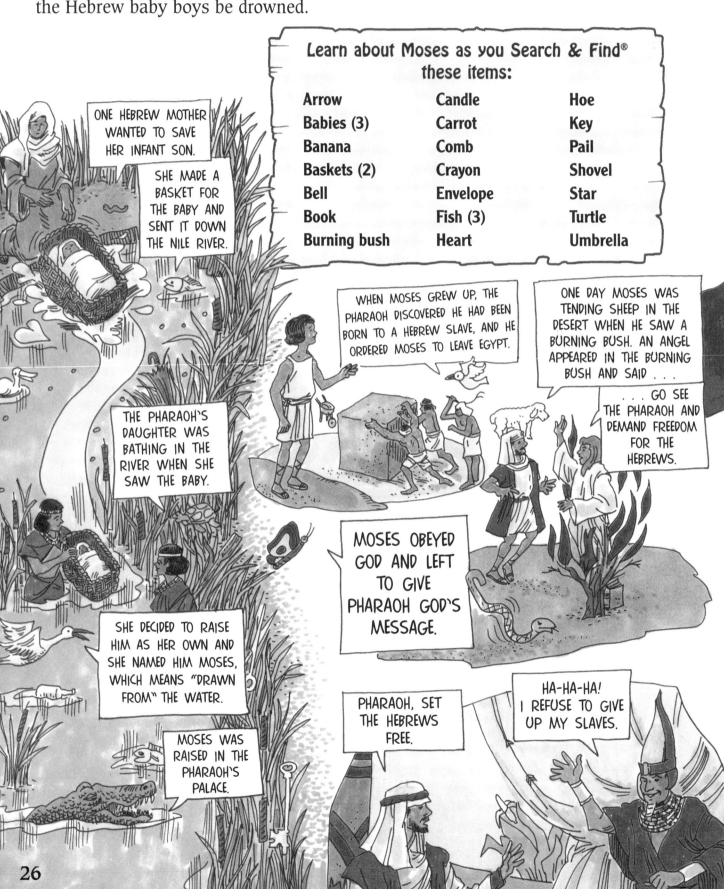

Learn about Moses as you Search & Find® these items:

Arrow	Candle	Hoe
Babies (3)	Carrot	Key
Banana	Comb	Pail
Baskets (2)	Crayon	Shovel
Bell	Envelope	Star
Book	Fish (3)	Turtle
Burning bush	Heart	Umbrella

ONE HEBREW MOTHER WANTED TO SAVE HER INFANT SON.

SHE MADE A BASKET FOR THE BABY AND SENT IT DOWN THE NILE RIVER.

THE PHARAOH'S DAUGHTER WAS BATHING IN THE RIVER WHEN SHE SAW THE BABY.

SHE DECIDED TO RAISE HIM AS HER OWN AND SHE NAMED HIM MOSES, WHICH MEANS "DRAWN FROM" THE WATER.

MOSES WAS RAISED IN THE PHARAOH'S PALACE.

WHEN MOSES GREW UP, THE PHARAOH DISCOVERED HE HAD BEEN BORN TO A HEBREW SLAVE, AND HE ORDERED MOSES TO LEAVE EGYPT.

ONE DAY MOSES WAS TENDING SHEEP IN THE DESERT WHEN HE SAW A BURNING BUSH. AN ANGEL APPEARED IN THE BURNING BUSH AND SAID . . .

. . . GO SEE THE PHARAOH AND DEMAND FREEDOM FOR THE HEBREWS.

MOSES OBEYED GOD AND LEFT TO GIVE PHARAOH GOD'S MESSAGE.

PHARAOH, SET THE HEBREWS FREE.

HA-HA-HA! I REFUSE TO GIVE UP MY SLAVES.

27

MOSES : PART II

As soon as the Hebrews left Egypt with Moses, the pharaoh changed his mind and ordered his army to recapture them. The army trapped them on the banks of the Red Sea. Moses raised his staff over the water and the sea parted.

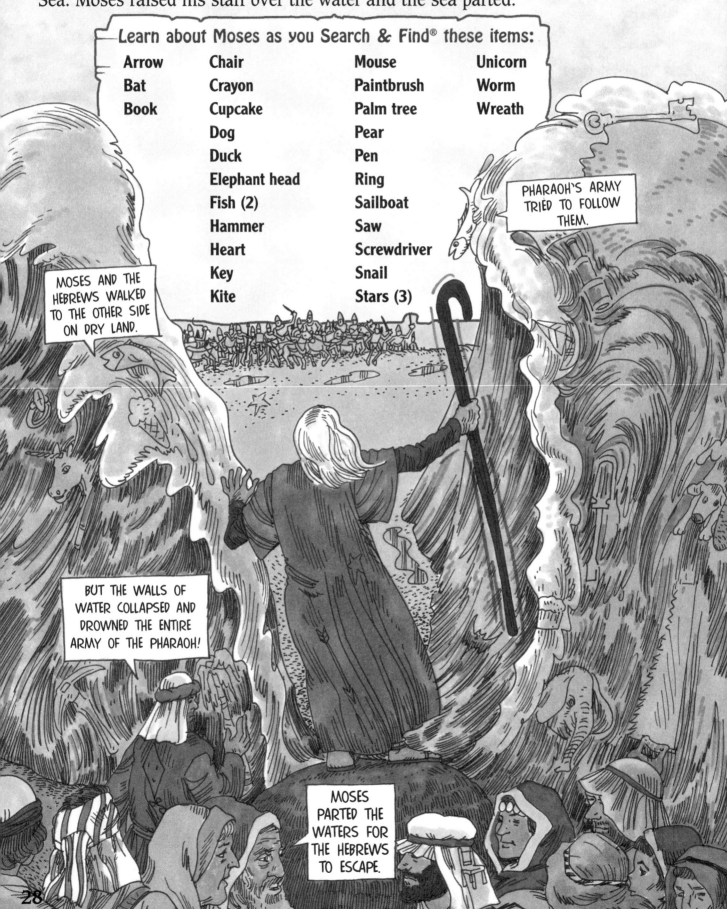

Learn about Moses as you Search & Find® these items:

Arrow	Chair	Mouse	Unicorn
Bat	Crayon	Paintbrush	Worm
Book	Cupcake	Palm tree	Wreath
	Dog	Pear	
	Duck	Pen	
	Elephant head	Ring	
	Fish (2)	Sailboat	
	Hammer	Saw	
	Heart	Screwdriver	
	Key	Snail	
	Kite	Stars (3)	

PHARAOH'S ARMY TRIED TO FOLLOW THEM.

MOSES AND THE HEBREWS WALKED TO THE OTHER SIDE ON DRY LAND.

BUT THE WALLS OF WATER COLLAPSED AND DROWNED THE ENTIRE ARMY OF THE PHARAOH!

MOSES PARTED THE WATERS FOR THE HEBREWS TO ESCAPE.

THE ARK OF THE LORD

While in the desert, the Hebrews worshipped God in a special tent called the Tabernacle. It had an inner room that contained the Ark of the Covenant. God told Moses exactly how to make the Ark.

Learn about the Ark as you Search & Find® these items:

Arrow	Chicken	Horse	Shovel
Axe	Cow	Paper airplane	Spears (6)
Books (2)	Dog	Penguin	Turtle
Butterflies (2)	Duck	Rabbit	Umbrella
Cake	Eagle	Red balloon	Worm
Carrot	Fish	Sheep	

THE ARK OF THE COVENANT IS A WOODEN CHEST LINED WITH GOLD.

IN THE MIDDLE OF THE LID IS "THE MERCY SEAT," WHERE GOD SITS WHEN HE WANTS TO SPEAK WITH PEOPLE.

ONLY ONE PERSON—THE HIGH PRIEST—IS ALLOWED TO LOOK INSIDE THE ARK.

ANYONE ELSE WHO LOOKS INSIDE WILL BE KILLED.

ABOVE THE TABERNACLE IS A SYMBOL OF GOD'S PRESENCE—A CLOUD BY DAY AND A PILLAR OF FIRE BY NIGHT.

INSIDE ARE THE TWO TABLETS OF THE TEN COMMANDMENTS.

ALSO INSIDE ARE 12 LOAVES OF BREAD, ONE FOR EACH OF THE HEBREW TRIBES.

NEW BREAD IS MADE EVERY WEEK, AND THE OLD BREAD IS SERVED ON A GOLDEN TRAY TO THE PRIESTS.

THE HEBREWS LOST THE ARK OF THE COVENANT WHILE THEY WERE FIGHTING A BATTLE AGAINST THEIR ENEMY, THE PHILISTINES.

WE PHILISTINES WILL TAKE THE ARK AND PUT IT IN THE TEMPLE OF OUR GOD, DAGON.

JOSHUA AND THE BATTLE OF JERICHO

Under Moses, the Hebrews wandered in the desert for 40 years. They complained to Moses and often argued with one another. Moses kept reminding them that they were God's chosen people. He knew that one day they would reach the Promised Land. Before they could get there, however, they had to conquer many strong-walled cities, including Jericho.

Learn about Joshua as you Search & Find® these items:

Apple	Fish (3)	Key	Snake
Bear	Flying ducks (3)	Kite	Tea bag
Book	Goat	Ladder	Teapot
Camel	Grapes	Palm tree	Turtle
Coffeepot	Hopping bunny	Pyramid	Umbrellas (3)
Elephant	Kangaroo	Sailboat	

GOD TOLD MOSES TO GO TO THE MOUNTAINS.

FROM A HIGH PEAK, GOD SHOWED MOSES CANAAN, THE PROMISED LAND—A LAND FLOWING WITH MILK AND HONEY.

THIS WAS THE LAND GOD PROMISED TO GIVE TO THE DESCENDANTS OF ABRAHAM, ISAAC, AND JACOB.

CANAAN STRETCHED FROM THE EUPHRATES RIVER IN THE EAST TO THE MEDITERRANEAN SEA IN THE WEST, AND FROM THE DESERT IN THE SOUTH TO THE MOUNTAINS OF LEBANON IN THE NORTH.

CANAAN WAS A RICH LAND FILLED WITH GRAPES, FIGS, AND POMEGRANATES.

MOSES DIED SOON AFTER GOD SHOWED HIM THE PROMISED LAND. HE WAS 120 YEARS OLD.

GOD CHOSE A NEW LEADER FOR THE HEBREWS. HIS NAME WAS JOSHUA.

JOSHUA WOULD LEAD THE HEBREWS ACROSS THE JORDAN RIVER TO CANAAN.

BUT FIRST, THE HEBREWS HAD TO CONQUER THE CITY OF JERICHO.

HEBREW SPIES TOLD JOSHUA THAT THE PEOPLE OF JERICHO WERE AFRAID OF THE HEBREWS.

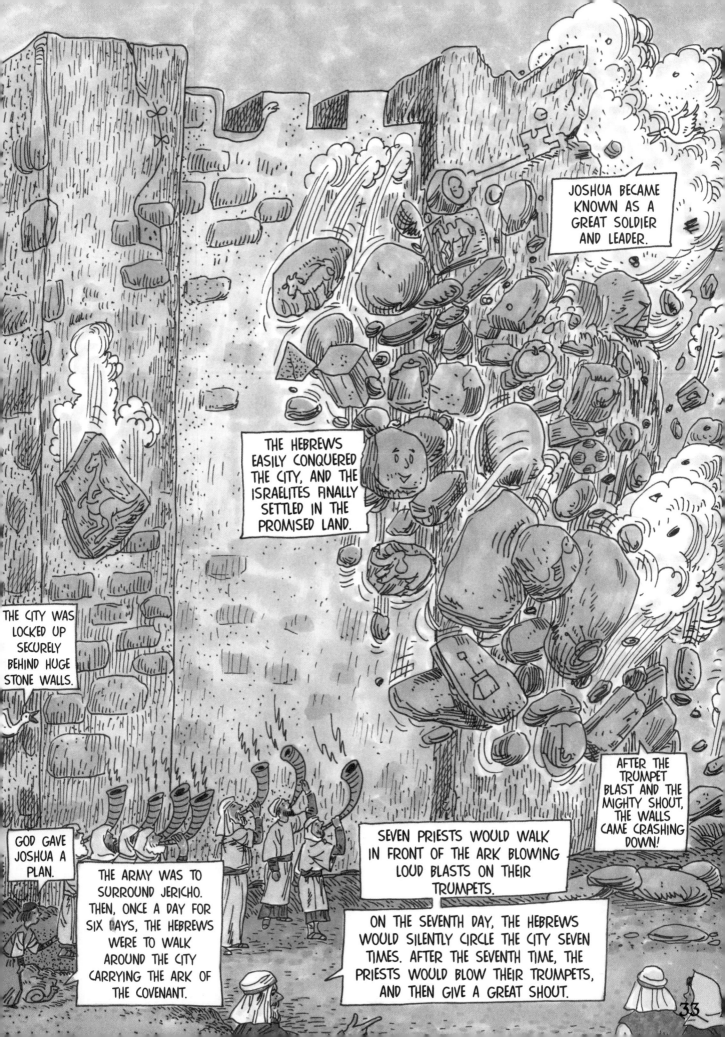

THE GREAT GIDEON

Gideon was a Hebrew judge. One day, God sent an angel to tell Gideon that he should lead a battle against the Midianites—a tribe that had conquered the Hebrews. The Midianites had burned the Hebrews' crops, and many people were in danger of starving. God had chosen Gideon to lead the battle because he was a very strong and brave man.

Learn about Gideon as you Search & Find® these items:

Axe	Horseshoe	Stars (2)
Candles (3)	Mouse	Sunflower
Club	Mushroom	Tepee
Dog	Music notes (2)	Turtle
Duck	Ring	Windmill
Fish	Sailboat	Worm
Frog	Shovel	
Guitar	Skull	

GIDEON WAS THRESHING WHEAT WHEN HE NOTICED AN ANGEL SITTING UNDER A TREE.

USE YOUR COURAGE TO FREE THE HEBREWS FROM THE POWER OF THE MIDIANITES.

WHEN GIDEON OFFERED FOOD TO THE ANGEL, THE ANGEL BURNED THE DISH WITH HIS STAFF. GIDEON KNEW THEN THAT THE ANGEL WAS SENT BY GOD.

GIDEON DESTROYED AN IDOL TO A FALSE GOD.

THE MIDIANITE ARMY GATHERED TOGETHER IN A VALLEY NEAR GIDEON'S HOME.

I'VE GATHERED AN ARMY OF 32,000 MEN, EVEN THOUGH GOD SAID I DO NOT NEED THAT MANY SOLDIERS.

GIDEON TOLD HIS TROOPS THAT ANYONE AFRAID TO FIGHT COULD LEAVE... 22,000 RAN HOME.

THE REMAINING 10,000 SOLDIERS WERE SENT TO A SPRING. MOST OF THEM PUT THEIR FACE TO THE WATER TO DRINK

THREE HUNDRED MEN SCOOPED UP THE WATER AND BROUGHT IT TO THEIR MOUTHS, LAPPING IT LIKE A DOG

GOD TOLD GIDEON TO KEEP ONLY THE MEN WHO SCOOPED UP THE WATER WITH THEIR HANDS.

GIDEON DIVIDED HIS MEN INTO THREE GROUPS.

EACH OF YOU MEN WILL HAVE A TRUMPET AND A JAR WITH A TORCH INSIDE IT.

THE HEBREWS RACED TOWARD THE MIDIANITE ARMY FROM ALL SIDES, BLOWING THEIR TRUMPETS, SMASHING THEIR JARS, AND WAVING THE TORCHES!

THE TERRIFIED MIDIANITES FLED, AND GIDEON'S ARMY WON THE BATTLE.

DAVID AND GOLIATH

David was a young Hebrew shepherd. While out in the fields, he practiced throwing rocks with his slingshot. David's older brothers were in the army of King Saul, fighting against the Philistines. The leader of the Philistines was a giant named Goliath.

Learn about David and Goliath as you Search & Find® these items:

Banana peel	Drum	Snake
Book	Hammer	Star
Broken egg	Key	Toothbrush
Broom	Pear	Trumpet
Cup	Rabbit	Umbrella
Deer	Slingshot	Yo-yo

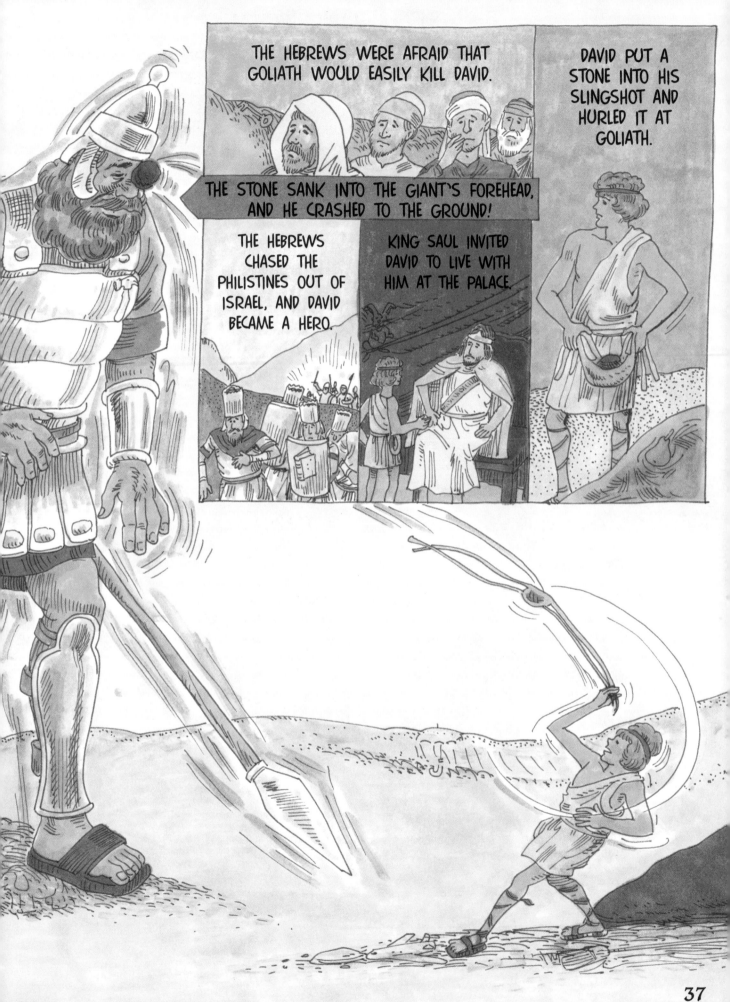

DAVID AND THE KING

While living in the palace, David and King Saul grew very close. Saul loved David like a son, and took pride in all that he did.

Learn about David and the king as you Search & Find® these items:

Apple	Cup	Heart	Owl	Swords (2)
Book	Fish	Ice-cream cone	Ring	Trumpet
Brush	Hammer	Mouse	Snake	Turtle
Candle	Harp	Music note	Stars (2)	Umbrella

KING SAUL OFTEN HAD BAD MOODS, AND DAVID PLAYED THE HARP TO SOOTHE HIM.

WHEN DAVID GREW UP, HE BECAME A FAMOUS SOLDIER, THE KING GREW JEALOUS OF HIM.

SAUL WAS WORRIED THAT THE HEBREW PEOPLE WOULD KILL HIM SO THAT DAVID COULD BE THEIR KING.

WHEN SAUL EVENTUALLY DIED IN BATTLE, DAVID DID BECOME KING.

KING DAVID WANTED TO BUILD A ROYAL CITY.

I WILL BUILD MY ROYAL CITY ON A MOUNTAIN. I WILL CALL IT JERUSALEM, WHICH MEANS CITY OF PEACE.

DAVID DECIDED TO BRING THE ARK OF THE COVENANT TO JERUSALEM AND PLACE IT SAFELY WITHIN THE CITY WALLS.

YEARS LATER, DAVID FELL IN LOVE WITH A BEAUTIFUL MARRIED WOMAN NAMED BATHSHEBA.

DAVID ARRANGED TO HAVE HER HUSBAND, A SOLDIER NAMED URIAH, KILLED IN BATTLE.

THEN DAVID MARRIED BATHSHEBA.

GOD PUNISHED DAVID FOR THIS BY HAVING BATHSHEBA'S FIRST SON DIE.

DAVID ASKED GOD FOR FORGIVENESS. GOD FORGAVE DAVID AND BLESSED THE COUPLE WITH A SECOND SON NAMED SOLOMON.

SOLOMON BECAME KING AFTER DAVID'S DEATH.

THE WISDOM OF KING SOLOMON

Solomon was one of Israel's youngest and greatest kings. He came to power after his father, David, died. David was the man who killed Goliath.

Learn about King Solomon as you Search & Find® these items:

Arrow	Cup	Flying bat	Kite
Bananas	Duck	Fork	Pear
Birdhouse	Elephant	Grapes	Shovel
Bone	Envelope	Heart	Stars (2)
Broom	Fish	Key	Umbrella

SOON AFTER SOLOMON BECAME KING, HE VISITED A PLACE NAMED GIBEON. THERE HE OFFERED GOD A SACRIFICE AND HAD AN IMPORTANT DREAM.

I APPRECIATE HOW MUCH YOU LOVED MY FATHER, DAVID. ISRAEL HAS MANY PEOPLE, AND I AM WORRIED ABOUT HOW I WILL RULE THEM.

I ASK YOU GOD FOR ONLY ONE THING—THE WISDOM TO RULE ISRAEL FAIRLY.

I AM PLEASED WITH YOUR CHOICE, SOLOMON.

I WILL GIVE YOU MORE WISDOM THAN ANY OTHER PERSON, AND I WILL ALSO MAKE YOU A VERY RICH MAN.

YOU WILL LIVE A LONG LIFE IF YOU OBEY ME.

THE NEXT DAY, SOLOMON GAVE A GREAT FEAST SO THAT HE AND HIS PEOPLE COULD THANK GOD.

BEAUTIFUL QUEEN ESTHER

Esther was the wife of the Persian king, Ahasuerus. Because of her great beauty, she was chosen to be his wife out of all the women in the kingdom.

WHEN ESTHER MARRIED THE KING, SHE DID NOT TELL HIM SHE WAS A HEBREW.

Learn about Queen Esther as you Search & Find® these items:

Arrow	Clipboard	Horseshoe	Star
Bird	Fish (2)	Lost sock	Tepee
Brush	Flower	Pencil	Toothbrush
Cactus	Goblet	Plate	Turtle
Candy cane	Hearts (2)	Saw	Whistle

SOON AFTER ESTHER BECAME QUEEN, HER COUSIN MORDECAI DISCOVERED A PLOT TO KILL THE KING.

MY COUSIN TOLD ME THERE IS A PLOT TO KILL YOU!

I WILL STOP THE PLOT. THANK MORDECAI FOR SAVING MY LIFE.

A WHILE LATER, ONE OF THE KING'S OFFICERS, HAMAN, WAS HONORED BY THE KING.

ALL MY SERVANTS MUST BOW DOWN TO HAMAN!

HAMAN WAS AN EVIL MAN. ALL HE WANTED WAS POWER.

MORDECAI CHOSE NOT TO BOW DOWN TO HAMAN. HE WOULD ONLY BOW DOWN TO GOD.

MORDECAI IS TO BE KILLED!

I URGE YOU TO PASS A NEW LAW THAT WILL CONDEMN TO DEATH ALL HEBREWS LIVING IN YOUR KINGDOM!

I MUST ACT TO SAVE MY PEOPLE.

QUEEN ESTHER WENT TO SEE THE KING, EVEN THOUGH HE HAD NOT SENT FOR HER. HER VISIT WAS PUNISHABLE BY DEATH.

I WISH TO INVITE YOU TO A DINNER THAT I WILL PREPARE FOR YOU.

I AM PROUD OF YOUR COURAGE AND ACCEPT YOUR INVITATION.

SAMSON AND DELILAH

Before Samson was born, an angel appeared to his parents and told them that Samson would do God's work. Samson's parents knew that God had great plans for him.

Learn about Samson as you Search & Find® these items:

Anchor	Book	Carrot	Flowerpot	Star
Axe	Broken	Cheese	Fork	Sticks
Bird	columns (2)	Comb	Heart	Tent
Birdcage	Butterfly	Drum	Scissors	Toothbrush
Bone	Candle	Fish	Snake	

AS A SIGN OF DEVOTION TO GOD, SAMSON NEVER CUT HIS HAIR.

IN RETURN, GOD GAVE SAMSON INCREDIBLE STRENGTH. WHEN SAMSON GREW UP, HIS HAIR WAS LONG, AND HIS STRENGTH WAS UNMATCHED.

HE WAS AS STRONG AS SEVEREAL MEN, HE COULD EVEN KILL A LION WITH HIS BARE HANDS.

ONE DAY, SAMSON MET DELILAH, A BEAUTIFUL AND CHARMING PHILISTINE WOMAN.

DELILAH HAD MADE AN ARRANGEMENT WITH THE PHILISTINES ...

WE WILL GIVE YOU GREAT RICHES IF YOU CAN FIND OUT WHY SAMSON IS SO STRONG!

SAMSON FELL IN LOVE WITH DELILAH.

WHY ARE YOU SO STRONG?

AFTER SHE ASKED HIM MANY TIMES, SAMSON FINALLY REVEALED HIS SECRET.

IF I CUT MY HAIR, I AM AS WEAK AS ANY OTHER MAN.

DELILAH IMMEDIATELY TOLD THE PHILISTINES, AND SAMSON WAS ARRESTED.

CUT OFF HIS HAIR!

POKE OUT HIS EYES!

THEY PUT HIM IN PRISON.

THE LEADER OF THE PHILISTINES MADE A GREAT FEAST. HE TIED SAMSON TO THE PILLARS OF HIS HOUSE SO THAT THE GUESTS COULD MOCK HIM.

BUT SAMSON'S HAIR HAD BEGUN TO GROW BACK, AND HE PRAYED THAT HIS STRENGTH WOULD RETURN ONE LAST TIME. SAMSON PUSHED AGAINST THE PILLARS OF THE HOUSE UNTIL THE ROOF CAVED IN. SAMSON AND ALL 3,000 PEOPLE INSIDE, WERE KILLED.

THE STORY OF RUTH

Ruth, a distant ancestor of Jesus, was also David's great-grandmother. She lived in Moab, a country near Judah.

RUTH'S HUSBAND WAS A MAN FROM MOAB. WHEN HE DIED, RUTH DECIDED TO STAY WITH NAOMI, HER MOTHER-IN-LAW.

WHERE YOU GO, I WILL GO.

Learn about Ruth as you Search & Find® these items:

Hearts (3)
Kites (3)
Knives (3)
Mushrooms (3)
Birds (3)
Paintbrushes (3)
Cloud
Spoons (3)
Cups (3)
Stars (3)
Fish (3)
Worms (3)

NAOMI DECIDED TO RETURN TO JUDAH, SO RUTH WENT WITH HER.

WHEN THEY ARRIVED, THEY WERE VERY POOR AND HUNGRY.

RUTH FOUND FOOD BY FOLLOWING PEOPLE WHO HARVESTED BARLEY FIELDS.

RUTH GATHERED THE GRAINS THAT THE HARVESTERS DROPPED ON THE GROUND AND TOOK THEM HOME TO NAOMI.

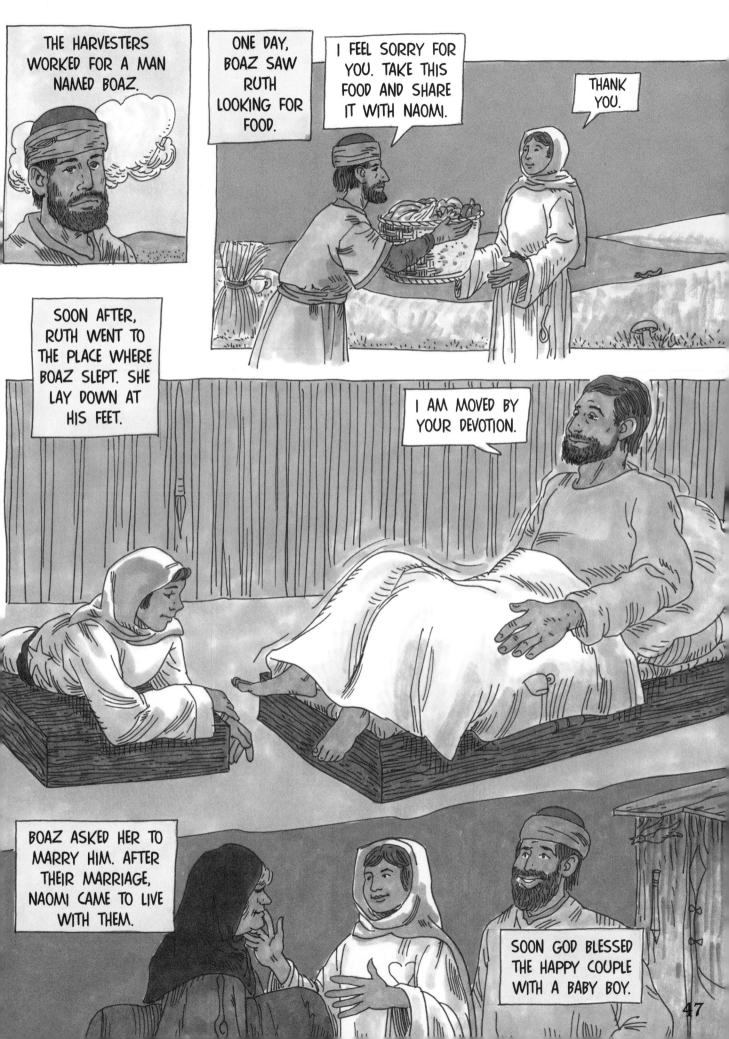

THE HARVESTERS WORKED FOR A MAN NAMED BOAZ.

ONE DAY, BOAZ SAW RUTH LOOKING FOR FOOD.

I FEEL SORRY FOR YOU. TAKE THIS FOOD AND SHARE IT WITH NAOMI.

THANK YOU.

SOON AFTER, RUTH WENT TO THE PLACE WHERE BOAZ SLEPT. SHE LAY DOWN AT HIS FEET.

I AM MOVED BY YOUR DEVOTION.

BOAZ ASKED HER TO MARRY HIM. AFTER THEIR MARRIAGE, NAOMI CAME TO LIVE WITH THEM.

SOON GOD BLESSED THE HAPPY COUPLE WITH A BABY BOY.

47

DANIEL IN THE DEN OF LIONS

When King Darius ruled Babylon, he gave Daniel an important position in the government. Daniel was known for being wise and honest. He did such a good job that King Darius wanted to put Daniel in charge of the whole Persian empire.

THE PERSIAN PEOPLE WORSHIPPED MANY FALSE GODS.

DANIEL KNEW THIS, BUT HE CONTINUED TO WORSHIP ONLY ONE GOD—THE GOD OF ISRAEL.

I PRAY TO GOD EVERY DAY.

MANY OF THE PEOPLE DANIEL WORKED WITH WERE JEALOUS OF HIM.

WE'RE ANGRY THAT A HEBREW HAS MORE POWER THAN WE DO!

OTHER PERSIAN OFFICIALS PLOTTED AGAINST DANIEL.

KING DARIUS, MAKE A LAW THAT WILL PUNISH ANYONE WHO PRAYS TO ANY GOD FOR THE NEXT THIRTY DAYS.

IF SOMEONE PRAYS, HE MUST BE THROWN INTO A DEN FILLED WITH LIONS.

I WILL MAKE THIS LAW, AND IT CANNOT BE CHANGED!

48

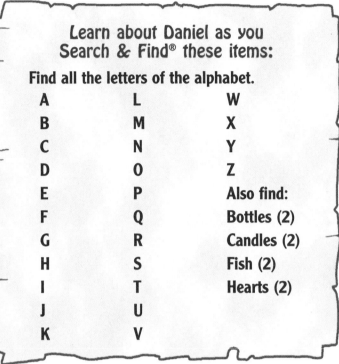

Learn about Daniel as you Search & Find® these items:

Find all the letters of the alphabet.

A	L	W
B	M	X
C	N	Y
D	O	Z
E	P	**Also find:**
F	Q	Bottles (2)
G	R	Candles (2)
H	S	Fish (2)
I	T	Hearts (2)
J	U	
K	V	

WHEN THE RULE BEGAN, DANIEL CONTINUED TO PRAY TO GOD.

I KNOW ABOUT THE LAW, BUT I WILL STILL PRAY.

THE OFFICIALS WENT TO THE KING AND TOLD ON DANIEL. THE KING WAS VERY SORRY. HE DID NOT WANT TO HURT DANIEL, BUT HE HAD TO OBEY HIS LAW.

ALL RIGHT. PUT DANIEL IN THE LION'S DEN.

I'M SORRY, DANIEL.

I HOPE YOUR GOD KEEPS YOU SAFE.

KING DARIUS DID NOT WANT DANIEL TO DIE.

THE NEXT MORNING, KING DARIUS WENT TO THE LION'S PIT.

DANIEL!

MY GOD SAVED ME!

GOD SENT AN ANGEL TO TAME THE LIONS.

DANIEL DOES NOT EVEN HAVE A SCRATCH!

I ORDER EVERYONE IN MY EMPIRE TO WORSHIP THE GOD OF ISRAEL.

DANIEL LIVED FOR MANY MORE YEARS AND CONTINUED TO WORSHIP GOD.

49

ELIJAH AND THE CHARIOT OF FIRE

Elijah was a prophet, a person who spoke for God. People visited Elijah to find out what would happen in the future.

ONE DAY, KING AHAB VISITED ELIJAH.

YOU WORSHIP BAAL, THE WRONG GOD. THERE WILL BE NO RAIN UNLESS YOU WORSHIP THE HEBREW GOD.

Learn about Elijah as you Search & Find® these items:

Axe	Cat	Rock in a stream
Bone	Chariots (2)	Shark fin
Book	Dog	Stars (5)
Broom	Hearts (2)	Unicorn
Camel	Owl	

I DO NOT BELIEVE YOU, ELIJAH. I WILL CONTINUE TO WORSHIP THE GOD BAAL.

KING AHAB'S KINGDOM HAD NO RAIN FOR THREE YEARS.

I CHALLENGE THE 400 PRIESTS OF BAAL TO ASK THEIR GOD TO LIGHT A FIRE.

THE PRIESTS WERE NOT ALLOWED TO USE FLINT OR ROCK. THE PRIESTS CALLED ON BAAL. NOTHING HAPPENED!

I WILL PROVE THAT THE HEBREW GOD IS MORE POWERFUL THAN BAAL.

I WILL PLACE TWO BULLS ON THIS ALTAR.

ELIJAH CALLED ON GOD. FIRE BLAZED!

I WAS WRONG! I WILL NOW PRAY TO THE HEBREW GOD!

RAIN FELL ON HIS KINGDOM.

REBUILDING THE WALL

After King Darius died, King Cyrus took over. By this time, the Hebrews had returned to Jerusalem.

KING CYRUS ALLOWED SOLOMON'S TEMPLE TO BE REBUILT.

KING CYRUS ALSO WANTED THE CITY WALLS TO BE REBUILT BECAUSE THE HEBREWS HAD MANY ENEMIES.

Learn about the wall as you Search & Find® these items:

Balloon	Envelope
Basket	Fish
Birdhouse	Fork
Bone	Heart
Book	Horseshoe
Bow and	Kite
arrow	Pigeon
Broom	Rooster
Butterfly	Ship
Cane	Shovel

NEHEMIAH, THE KING'S CUPBEARER, WAS IN CHARGE OF CONSTRUCTION.

THE RUINED WALLS LEAVE JERUSALEM OPEN TO ATTACK. THAT IS WHY I HAVE SECRETLY SENT FOR YOU SOLDIERS.

HE DIVIDED THEM INTO GROUPS OF WORKERS AND GUARDS.

I AM GIVING EACH OF YOU GUARDS A HORN.

JONAH AND THE WHALE

There was once a city named Ninevah. The people who lived there were wicked, and God was upset with them.

Learn about Jonah as you Search & Find® these items:

Cane	Hammer	Piggybank
Crown	Ice skate	Shovel
Crutch	Key	Spoon
Duck	Lost shoe	Stars (2)
Feather	Lost sock	Turtle
Fish (3)	Mouse	Umbrella

GOD WANTED THE PEOPLE TO CHANGE THEIR WAYS, SO HE ASKED A MAN NAMED JONAH TO TRAVEL TO NINEVEH.

GOD WANTED JONAH TO TELL THE PEOPLE TO OBEY HIS COMMANDMENTS.

I DO NOT WANT TO GO TO NINEVEH! I WILL NOT OBEY GOD!

JONAH SET OUT ON A BOAT IN THE OPPOSITE DIRECTION FROM NINEVEH.

GOD WILL NOT FIND ME.

ON THE BOAT, JONAH FELL ASLEEP. WHILE HE SLEPT, A TERRIBLE STORM STARTED.

ALL THOSE ON BOARD WERE SCARED THEY WOULD DROWN. THEY PRAYED TO GOD TO SAVE THEM.

THE STORM IS MY FAULT.

GOD WAS ANGRY BECAUSE JONAH WAS RUNNING AWAY.

THROW ME OVERBOARD, AND THE STORM WILL STOP.

AT FIRST, THE PEOPLE WOULD NOT TOSS JONAH OVERBOARD.

WE'LL ROW HARDER.

WE STILL CANNOT REACH THE SHORE!

SO THEY TOSSED JONAH INTO THE OCEAN.

THEN THE STORM CLEARED.

WHILE JONAH WAS IN THE WATER, GOD SENT A WHALE! THE WHALE SWALLOWED JONAH!

JONAH WAS INSIDE THE WHALE FOR THREE DAYS AND THREE NIGHTS.

AFTER THAT TIME, JONAH TOLD GOD HE WAS SORRY.

GO TO NINEVEH!

JONAH WAS TO TELL PEOPLE THAT GOD WOULD DESTROY THEIR CITY IF THEY DID NOT CHANGE.

I WILL GO TO NINEVEH.

HE SPREAD GOD'S MESSAGE, AND EVERYONE BELIEVED HIM!

EVERYONE MUST PRAY TO GOD AND REPENT.

I AM PLEASED THAT THE PEOPLE HAVE CHANGED. I FORGIVE YOU ALL.

BUT JONAH WAS NOT HAPPY.

GOD, I WANT YOU TO PUNISH THE PEOPLE!

ARE YOU SAD WHEN YOU SEE A PLANT DIE?

YES!

THE PEOPLE OF NINEVEH ARE LIKE PLANTS!

I LOVE THESE PEOPLE. IF YOU CARE ABOUT PLANTS, YOU SHOULD CARE ABOUT PEOPLE.

NOW I FINALLY UNDERSTAND WHY GOD SENT ME TO NINEVEH!

THE LAST JUDGE AND THE FIRST KING

Thousands of years ago, a woman named Hannah prayed to God for a child. She promised God that if He granted her request, she would give her child to the Lord for all the days of his life.

SOON AFTER, HANNAH GAVE BIRTH TO SAMUEL.

KEEPING HER PROMISE, HANNAH TOOK HER SON TO LIVE WITH ELI, A NEARBY PRIEST.

Learn about the last judge and the first king as you Search & Find® these items:

Balloon	Chef's hat	Owl
Book	Fish (2)	Sailboat
Broom	Heart	Scroll
Bucket	Jack-o'-lantern	Seal
Cactus	Kite	Stars (2)
Camel	Lost sock	Turtle
Cane	Oilcan	Unicorn

SAMUEL WAS A HELPER TO ELI, A PRIEST AT THE TEMPLE.

ONE NIGHT, GOD CALLED TO SAMUEL. HEARING A VOICE, SAMUEL RAN TO ELI'S ROOM..

HERE I AM, ELI. YOU CALLED ME?

RETURN TO YOUR BED. I DID NOT CALL YOU!

A FEW MINUETS LATER, SAMUEL HEARD THE VOICE AGAIN. HE RETURNED TO ELI'S ROOM. ELI NOW KNEW . . .

IF THE VOICE SPEAKS TO YOU AGAIN, SAY: "SPEAK, LORD."

GOD CALLED TO SAMUEL A THIRD TIME.

SPEAK, LORD.

GOD TOLD SAMUEL SOME THINGS THAT WERE ABOUT TO HAPPEN.

YEARS LATER, SAMUEL BECAME ONE OF THE BEST JUDGES THE HEBREWS EVER HAD.

WHEN HE WAS OLD, SAMUEL APPOINTED HIS SONS, JOEL AND ABIJAH, AS JUDGES FOR ISRAEL.

BUT THEY WERE NOT HONEST LIKE SAMUEL. THEY TOOK BRIBES AND MADE BAD JUDGEMENTS.

BECAUSE OF THIS, PEOPLE NO LONGER WANTED JUDGES TO RULE OVER THEM.

SAMUEL, WE WANT YOU TO NAME A KING.

GOD HAS LED ME TO YOU, SAUL. YOU WILL BE THE FIRST KING.

YOU HAVE MADE ME THE KING.

SAUL WAS AN HONEST MAN WHO RULED THE ISRAELITES FOR MANY YEARS.

SAUL WON MANY BATTLES AGAINST THE PHILISTINES.

SAUL HAS DEFEATED US AGAIN.

BUT SAUL ALSO DISOBEYED GOD'S ORDERS MANY TIMES. EVENTUALLY GOD BECAME DISPLEASED WITH SAUL.

WHEN SAUL DIED, DAVID, THE SLAYER OF GOLIATH, BECAME KING.

57

WOMEN WARRIORS

The Hebrews were ruled by a series of judges, not a single leader. The judges were men and women who settled legal problems as well as quarrels.

DEBORAH WAS A JUDGE AND A MILITARY LEADER.

ONE DAY, AN ENEMY NAMED SISERA THREATENED THE HEBREWS.

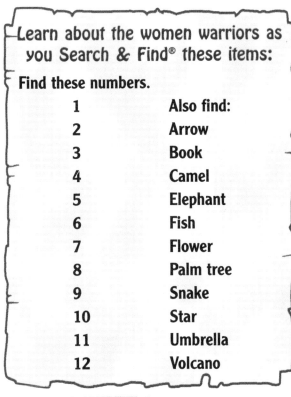

Learn about the women warriors as you Search & Find® these items:

Find these numbers.

1	**Also find:**
2	**Arrow**
3	**Book**
4	**Camel**
5	**Elephant**
6	**Fish**
7	**Flower**
8	**Palm tree**
9	**Snake**
10	**Star**
11	**Umbrella**
12	**Volcano**

DEBORAH WENT TO BARAK, THE LEADER OF THE ISRAELITE ARMY.

YOU MUST ATTACK SISERA.

SISERA HAS MORE THAN 900 CHARIOTS.

BARAK THOUGHT DEBORAH WAS FOOLISH TO THINK THEY COULD WIN. BUT, HE TOLD HER . . .

IF YOU COME, I WILL GO!

I WILL!

TOGETHER, DEBORAH AND BARAK LED 10,000 SOLDIERS TO VICTORY.

AFTER SISERA'S ARMY WAS DEFEATED, SISERA TRIED TO GO INTO HIDING. HE HID IN THE TENT OF A WOMAN NAMED JAEL.

JAEL HELPED SISERA BY DRESSING HIS WOUNDS, AND GIVING HIM FOOD.

BUT WHEN SISERA FELL ASLEEP, JAEL DROVE A TENT PEG INTO HIS HEAD.

DEBORAH AND BARAK PRAISED JAEL FOR KILLING SISERA.

NEW TESTAMENT

THE ANGEL GABRIEL

The angel Gabriel brought news of heavenly babies to women who could not have children.

THE BIRTH OF JESUS

Two thousand years ago, a young woman named Mary lived in the town of Nazareth. One day, an angel from heaven came to Mary and gave her a message from God. The angel told Mary she was going to have a baby. The baby's name would be Jesus, and He would be God's son.

Learn about the birth of Jesus as you Search & Find® these items:

Candle	Key	Ring
Cow	Lantern	Saw
Drum	Mouse	Screwdriver
Feather	Music note	Shovel
Fish	Owls (2)	Sock
Hearts (3)	Paintbrush	Toothbrush
Horseshoe	Rabbits (2)	Umbrella

65

THE VOICE IN THE WILDERNESS

Many years before Jesus was born, a prophet named Isaiah made a prediction. He said that someday a man would cry in the wilderness with a loud voice. This man would prepare a path for the Lord.

Learn about the voice in the wilderness as you Search & Find® these items:

Ball
Banana peel
Barbell
Birdcage
Birds (2)
Bone
Book

Elephant
Fish
Hearts (2)
Horse
Horseshoe
Key
Mouse

Owl
Paper airplane
Snake
Turtle
Umbrella

MANY YEARS LATER, JUST AS ISAIAH PREDICTED, A MAN NAMED JOHN BEGAN TO PREACH.

THE SAVIOR OF THE JEWS IS COMING!

HE LIVES IN THE DESERT AND WEARS CLOTHES MADE OF CAMEL'S HAIR.

HE IS KNOWN AS "JOHN THE BAPTIST." HE TRAVELS ALL OVER THE COUNTRYSIDE TELLING THE PEOPLE TO REPENT.

SOME PEOPLE THINK THAT JOHN IS THE SAVIOR.

JOHN ALWAYS TELLS THEM HE IS NOT.

ONE OF JOHN'S TEACHINGS IS TO BAPTIZE PEOPLE.

BAPTIZE MEANS TO PURIFY A PERSON'S SPIRIT, OFTEN BY USING WATER.

HE BAPTIZED PEOPLE BY WASHING THEM IN THE RIVER JORDAN TO CLEANSE THEM OF THEIR SINS.

HE EATS ONLY WILD HONEY AND OATS.

HE TELLS PEOPLE TO APOLOGIZE FOR THEIR SINS. IF PEOPLE APOLOGIZE OR REPENT, GOD WILL FORGIVE THEM.

THE TEMPTATIONS OF JESUS

One day, the Holy Spirit led Jesus into the wilderness. Once there, Jesus did not eat or drink anything for 40 days. This is called fasting. While Jesus fasted, the devil tried to tempt Him three times.

Learn about the temptations of Jesus as you Search & Find® these items:

- Alligator
- Apple
- Bird's nest
- Butterfly
- Crayon
- Cupcake
- Fish
- Hammer
- Heart
- Kite
- Mailbox
- Moon crest
- Music notes (4)
- Paintbrush
- Pencils (2)
- Snake
- Star
- Tulip

FIRST SATAN TRIED TO TEMPT JESUS BY MAKING HIM TURN STONES TO BREAD.

IF YOU REALLY ARE THE SON OF GOD, TURN THESE ROCKS INTO BREAD.

A PERSON DOES NOT LIVE ONLY BY EATING BREAD. A PERSON LIVES BY OBEYING GOD.

EVEN THOUGH JESUS WAS HUNGRY, HE WOULD NOT DO WHAT SATAN WANTED.

NEXT, SATAN TOOK JESUS TO THE HIGHEST POINT ON THE TEMPLE IN JERUSALEM.

I CHALLENGE YOU TO THROW YOURSELF FROM THE TOP OF THE TEMPLE.

IF YOU ARE THE SON OF GOD, THEN GOD WILL PROTECT YOU.

SATAN WAS GETTING WORRIED. HE TRIED TO TEMPT JESUS ONE LAST TIME.

69

JESUS FINDS THE APOSTLES

One day, John the Baptist was arrested by King Herod. At the time, Jesus was about 30 years old. John the Baptist began preaching to the people. He preached for three years before he died.

Learn about the apostles as you Search & Find® these items:

Balloon	Fishing pole	Sled
Barrel	Flower	Snail
Bat	Kite	Sock
Birdhouse	Mitten	Stars (2)
Broom	Mouse	Turtle
Candle	Sewing needle	White birds (2)

ONE DAY, JESUS WAS PREACHING NEAR THE SEA OF GALILEE.

SIMON, TAKE ME OUT IN YOUR FISHING BOAT.

NOW I CAN PREACH TO ALL THE PEOPLE WHO HAVE GATHERED TO HEAR ME.

AFTER JESUS FINISHED PRAYING, HE TOLD SIMON TO DROP THE FISHING NETS INTO THE WATER.

WHEN SIMON LIFTED THE NETS, THEY WERE FILLED WITH FISH.

YOU ARE NOW FISHERS OF MEN.

THE NETS WERE SO HEAVY THAT THEY ALMOST SANK THE SHIP.

AFTER UNLOADING THE NETS, SIMON AND THREE OTHER FISHERMEN BECAME FOLLOWERS.

OTHER PEOPLE ALSO FOLLOWED JESUS. THEY WERE KNOWN AS DISCIPLES.

THE WEDDING FEAST AT CANA

One day, Jesus and His family attended a wedding in Cana. Weddings were huge celebrations. They could last from a few days to a whole week. The guests at the wedding in Cana were full of joy. They were dancing and laughing. They were also eating and drinking wine to rejoice with the newly married couple.

Learn about the wedding feast at Cana as you Search & Find® these items:

Balloon	Happy face	Mouse
Butterfly	Horseshoe	Pumpkin
Cat	Key	Stars (5)
Earmuffs	Kite	Toothbrush
Envelope	Milk container	Wine jugs (6)

THIS IS A MUCH LARGER CELEBRATION THAN WE HAD PLANNED.

ONLY A FEW HOURS INTO OUR FEAST AND WE'VE RUN OUT OF WINE.

I'M THE WINE STEWARD . . . WHAT CAN I DO?

HOW CAN PEOPLE CELEBRATE WITHOUT A FESTIVE DRINK?

MARY KNEW THAT JESUS COULD FIX THIS PROBLEM.

THE SERVANTS MUST DO WHATEVER JESUS ASKS OF THEM.

THE PRODIGAL SON

People often had questions for Jesus. Many times, they asked Jesus why He was willing to forgive and love people no matter how many mistakes they made. Jesus taught them by telling a story. A story that teaches is called a parable.

Learn about the Prodigal Son parable as you Search & Find® these items:

Birdcage	Hammer	Rope climber	Toothbrush
Bone	Hearts (3)	Shark fin	Turtle
Brush	Horseshoe	Snail	Umbrella
Donkey	Key	Snake	
Fish (2)	Rabbit	Tent	

THERE WAS ONCE A MAN WHO OWNED A BIG FARM.

HE HAD TWO SONS WHOM HE LOVED VERY MUCH.

ONE DAY, THE YOUNGER SON WENT TO HIS FATHER AND SAID THAT HE WANTED TO LEAVE HOME AND SEE THE WORLD.

THE YOUNGER SON ASKED HIS FATHER FOR MONEY SO HE COULD TRAVEL. THE FATHER LOVED HIS YOUNGER SON, SO HE GAVE HIM MONEY FOR THE TRIP.

THE YOUNGER SON WENT FAR AWAY. HIS BROTHER, THE OLDER SON, STAYED WITH THEIR FATHER AND WORKED ON THE FARM.

WHILE HE WAS AWAY, THE YOUNGER SON WASTED HIS MONEY ON SILLY THINGS. SOON, HIS MONEY RAN OUT.

POOR AND HOPELESS, HE FOUND WORK ON A FARM. HIS JOB WAS TO FEED THE PIGS.

THE YOUNG MAN WAS VERY UPSET ABOUT HIS LIFE.

HIS CLOTHES WERE TORN AND DIRTY, AND HE WAS OFTEN HUNGRY.

ONE DAY, THE YOUNG MAN QUIT HIS JOB.

HE LEFT TO RETURN HOME AND BEG HIS FATHER'S FORGIVENESS.

WHEN THE FATHER SAW HIS SON COMING UP THE ROAD, HE RAN TO HIM AND HUGGED AND KISSED HIM.

MY YOUNGEST SON!

THE YOUNG MAN APOLOGIZED TO HIS FATHER AND ASKED FOR FORGIVENESS. THE HAPPY FATHER CALLED FOR HIS SERVANTS TO PREPARE A CELEBRATION.

KILL THE FATTEST CALF ON THE FARM TO FEED MY SON. BRING HIM NEW CLOTHES AND SHOES AND A RING FOR HIS FINGER.

SOON THE OLDER SON CAME BACK FROM WORKING ALL DAY IN THE FIELDS. HE ASKED A SERVANT . . .

WHY IS EVERYONE CELEBRATING?

YOUR YOUNGER BROTHER HAS RETURNED.

THE OLDER BROTHER DECIDED NOT TO GO TO THE CELEBRATION.

WHY ARE YOU UPSET?

I DO NOT UNDERSTAND WHY ANYONE WOULD CELEBRATE. MY YOUNGER BROTHER WAS WASTEFUL. I HAVE WORKED HARD FOR YOU MY WHOLE LIFE.

I HAVE NEVER ONCE COMPLAINED, BUT I HAVE NOT BEEN GIVEN A PARTY.

I LOVE YOU ALWAYS. I AM GLAD YOU HAVE STAYED WITH ME.

EVERYONE MUST BE HAPPY BECAUSE YOUR YOUNGER BROTHER WAS ONCE LOST, BUT HE HAS RETURNED AND THE FAMILY IS TOGETHER AGAIN.

NOW I UNDERSTAND.

JESUS TOLD THIS STORY BECAUSE GOD IS LIKE THE FATHER IN THE STORY. HE LOVES EVERYONE AND WILL ALWAYS WELCOME EVERYONE BACK TO HIS FAMILY.

THE GOOD SAMARITAN

One day, Jesus was preaching to a crowd of people. A man in the crowd asked Jesus a question: "What do I need to do to go to heaven?" Jesus answered the man's question with another question.

WHAT DO THE TEN COMMANDMENTS SAY YOU SHOULD DO?

THEY TELL ME TO LOVE GOD ABOVE ALL ELSE, AND TO LOVE MY NEIGHBOR AS MYSELF.

Learn about the Good Samaritan as you Search & Find® these items:

Banana	Fox	Ring
Candles (4)	Hearts (3)	Stars (3)
Cross	Key	Turtle
Elephant	Music note	
Fish (2)	Rabbit	

THE MAN UNDERSTOOD HOW TO LOVE GOD. BUT THEN THE MAN ASKED JESUS ...

WHO IS MY NEIGHBOR?

I WILL TELL YOU A PARABLE SO YOU WILL UNDERSTAND.

ONE DAY, A JEWISH MAN WAS TRAVELING ON A ROAD FROM JERUSALEM TO JERICHO.

SUDDENLY, ROBBERS ATTACKED THE MAN. THEY STOLE HIS MONEY AND CLOTHES. THEN THEY HURT THE MAN, LEAVING HIM ON THE ROAD TO DIE.

SOON AFTER, A PRIEST CAME BY. HE SAW THE MAN, BUT HE DID NOT STOP. INSTEAD, HE HURRIED OFF, IGNORING THE DYING MAN.

SOON, ANOTHER TRAVELER CAME BY. HE SAW THE MAN, TOO, BUT HE CROSSED THE ROAD AND CONTINUED ON.

A FEW MINUTES LATER, A MAN FROM SAMARIA CAME ALONG. THE JEWS AND SAMARITANS HATED EACH OTHER.

BUT THIS SAMARITAN FELT BAD FOR THE DYING MAN. HE STOPPED AND BANDAGED THE MAN'S WOUNDS.

THEN THE SAMARITAN LIFTED THE MAN ONTO HIS HORSE AND TOOK HIM TO AN INN.

HE RENTED A ROOM FOR THE HURT MAN AND PAID FOR HIS FOOD AND NEW CLOTHES. HE MADE SURE THE INNKEEPER WOULD TAKE GOOD CARE OF THE MAN.

THE SAMARITAN LEFT FOR HIS JOURNEY, PROMISING TO RETURN AND CHECK ON THE MAN.

WHO REALLY LOVED HIS NEIGHBOR?

THE MAN FROM SAMARIA, THE ONE WHO WAS KIND.

JESUS TOLD THIS STORY TO SHOW THAT EVERYONE IS A NEIGHBOR TO EVERYONE ELSE. PEOPLE MUST LOVE THEIR NEIGHBORS, EVEN IF THEY ARE STRANGERS.

RAISING LAZARUS AND OTHER MIRACLES

Jesus knew many people because He traveled to a lot of cities. Three of His very close friends were Mary, Martha, and Lazarus, who were brother and sisters. They lived in a town named Bethany.

Learn about Jesus' miracles as you Search & Find® these items:

Axe	Candle	Hoe
Balloon	Cross	Horseshoe
Bell	Fish (2)	Paintbrush
Bird	Guitar	Sailboat
Bone	Hammer	Umbrella
Bush	Hearts (2)	

ONE DAY, JESUS WAS IN BETHANY VISITING LAZARUS AND HIS SISTERS. HE SPENT THE DAY IN THEIR HOME.

I'VE BEEN HERE A FEW DAYS NOW, AND IT IS TIME FOR ME TO LEAVE AND TEACH AT ANOTHER CITY.

WE HAVE NEWS FOR YOU, JESUS. IT'S FROM MARTHA AND MARY. LAZARUS IS SICK.

THEY ASK THAT YOU RETURN TO BETHANY TO HEAL LAZARUS.

I CANNOT LEAVE RIGHT AWAY.

HE STAYED TWO MORE DAYS IN THE OTHER CITY SO HE COULD TEACH.

JESUS KNEW THAT LAZARUS' SICKNESS WOULD NOT END IN DEATH. DAYS LATER, JESUS RETURNED TO BETHANY.

OH JESUS, LAZARUS HAS DIED!

YOUR BROTHER WILL LIVE AGAIN, MARTHA.

MANY PEOPLE WERE SAD ABOUT LAZARUS' DEATH.

THE MIRACLE OF THE LOAVES AND THE FISHES

One day, Jesus gathered together the twelve apostles and gave them a new power. He gave them the ability to perform miracles and cure the sick. Then He sent them on journeys to perform miracles in His name.

Learn about Jesus' miracles as you Search & Find® these items:

Apple
Arrow
Bird
Bone
Giraffe

Heart
Pencil
Pumpkin
Sailboat (2)
Snake

Star
Turtle
Umbrella
Watermelon slice

WHEN THE APOSTLES RETURNED, THEY WANTED TO SHARE THEIR STORIES WITH JESUS.

A LOCAL FISHERMAN SAID HE KNEW A QUIET PLACE WHERE THEY COULD BE ALONE TO TALK.

I WILL TAKE YOU ACROSS THE SEA OF GALILEE.

A LARGE CROWD WAS WAITING FOR THEM ON THE OTHER SIDE.

WE ALL WANT TO MEET JESUS.

HE HAS ARRIVED!

JESUS SPENT THE DAY TALKING WITH THE PEOPLE.

IT IS NOW EVENING, JESUS. SEND THE PEOPLE TO A NEARBY VILLAGE WHERE THEY CAN HAVE A MEAL AND FIND A PLACE TO REST.

JESUS WANTED TO TEST THE APOSTLES' FAITH IN HIM.

THE PEOPLE DO NOT HAVE TO LEAVE. YOU CAN GIVE THEM SOMETHING TO EAT.

JESUS, WE ARE CONFUSED.

ANDREW REMEMBERED SEEING A BOY WHO HAD FIVE LOAVES OF BREAD AND TWO FISH.

BUT THAT IS NOT ENOUGH TO FEED THOUSANDS OF PEOPLE.

WHEN JESUS MET THE BOY, HE TOOK THE BASKET OF FOOD.

81

JESUS AND THE PHARISEES

Although Jesus loved everyone, He did have some enemies. The Pharisees were part of a powerful religious group. They did not believe in the teachings of Jesus, and they disagreed with Him. They thought Jesus did not follow religious law strictly enough. They disapproved of Jesus preaching to Samaritans, tax collectors, and sinners.

Learn about Jesus and the Pharisees as you Search & Find® these items:

Arrow	Ring
Bat	Screwdriver
Bird	Shoe
Bottle	Shovel
Candles (3)	Tent
Cupcake	Toothbrush
Donkey	Tulip
Fish	Umbrella
Hammer	Unicorn
Heart	Volcano
Mouse	Watermelon slice

83

JESUS IN JERUSALEM

Jesus was traveling to Jerusalem to teach and pray. The people knew He was coming, so they decided to honor Him. Today this event is known as Palm Sunday.

Learn about Jesus in Jerusalem as you Search & Find® these items:

Arrow
Birds (2)
Candles (2)
Chicken
Dog
Duck
Fish (2)

Hearts (2)
Key
Lost sandal
Melting snowman
Owl
Paintbrush
Palm tree

Pennant
Stack of coins
Star
Tepee
Umbrella

JESUS IS RIDING INTO THE CITY ON A DONKEY.

LET'S SPREAD OUR CLOTHES ON THE GROUND BEFORE HIM.

WE'VE ALSO CUT BRANCHES OFF THE TREES AND SPREAD THESE IN HIS PATH.

BOTH THE CLOTHES AND THE LEAVES SHOW OUR RESPECT FOR JESUS!

WELCOME!

HE'S HERE!

IT'S JESUS!

85

THE LAST SUPPER

During Passover, Jesus and His apostles were making plans for a celebration. Like all the Hebrew people, they were planning a Passover supper, which is called a seder.

Learn about the Last Supper as you Search & Find® these items:

Candles (12)
Crosses (12)
Hearts (12)

ON THE MORNING OF THE FEAST, THE APOSTLES WERE DECIDING WHERE TO HOLD THE CELEBRATION.

GO TO JERUSALEM AND MEET A MAN WHO IS CARRYING A JUG OF WATER.

THE APOSTLES MET THE MAN, WHO TOOK THEM TO A HOUSE.

THE APOSTLES PREPARED FOR THE FEAST IN A LARGE UPPER ROOM IN THIS HOUSE. JESUS ARRIVED IN THE EVENING.

I AM HAPPY TO SHARE THIS MEAL WITH MY APOSTLES.

IT WILL BE A LONG TIME BEFORE WE EAT TOGETHER AGAIN.

THE GARDEN OF GETHSEMANE

After Jesus and the apostles finished their feast, they went to a garden called Gethsemane. Some of the apostles relaxed while Jesus strolled through the garden with James, John, and Peter.

JAMES, JOHN, AND PETER, I MUST TELL YOU I AM SAD.

Learn about what happened in the Garden of Gethsemane as you Search & Find® these items:

Candles (3)
Crosses (2)
Fish (2)
Flower

Hearts (3)
Quarter moons (2)
Stars (4)
Turtles (2)

JESUS KNEW WHAT WAS GOING TO HAPPEN THE NEXT DAY.

OFFICIALS WERE WORRIED ABOUT JESUS' POWER.

WE ARE ANGRY THAT PEOPLE THINK JESUS IS THE SAVIOR.

JESUS KNEW THAT HE WAS GOING TO BE HARMED.

JESUS RETURNED TO HIS APOSTLES. HE FOUND THEM ASLEEP.

I AM DISAPPOINTED IN YOU. I NEED YOU TO STAY AWAKE.

GOD GIVE ME COURAGE AND STRENGTH.

WAKE UP!

PETER, BEFORE THE ROOSTER CROWS THREE TIMES YOU WILL DISOWN ME.

THE MAN WHO WILL BETRAY ME IS WITH US IN THE GARDEN.

THE CRUCIFIXION

The next day, soldiers put a crown of thorns on Jesus' head. Then they made Him carry the wooden cross from which He would hang. The cross was very heavy. Jesus had to drag it through the streets of Jerusalem. When Jesus stumbled, a man called Simon carried the cross for Him.

Learn about the crucifixion as you Search & Find® these items:

Apples (2)   Fish (2)   Hearts (2)   Wooden
Brushes (2)   Flowers (2)   Ring   crosses (7)
Candles (2)   Hammer   Stars (2)

THE RESURRECTION

The Jewish sabbath begins at sundown. During the sabbath, people rest, and they do not work. Jesus was crucified during the sabbath. There was not enough time to rub His body with special oils before He was buried.

THE SABBATH ENDED ON SUNDAY MORNING AT SUNRISE. MARY MAGDALENE AND TWO OTHER WOMEN WENT TO JESUS' TOMB.

Learn about the Resurrection as you Search & Find® these items:

Broken heart	Key
Brush	Kite
Candle	Nail
Cross	Owl
Fish	Star
Hearts (2)	Teardrop

WE WILL GO SEE WHERE JESUS IS BURIED.

HOW WILL WE MOVE THE ROCK THAT IS BLOCKING THE TOMB'S ENTRANCE?

THE ROCK HAS BEEN MOVED!

A MAN WAS SITTING BY THE PLACE WHERE JESUS' BODY WAS LAID TO REST. JESUS' BODY WAS NOT THERE.

JESUS HAS RISEN FROM THE DEAD.

THE APOSTLES CAME AND SAW THAT JESUS' BODY WAS GONE. THE CLOTH PEOPLE HAD WRAPPED AROUND HIS BODY WAS ALSO GONE.

WE MUST FIND JESUS.

MARY MAGDALENE WEPT AS SHE LEFT THE TOMB.

ARE YOU ALL RIGHT?

I AM LOOKING FOR JESUS.

MARY!